PLEASANTVILLE 1893®

PLEASANTVILLE
1893 ®

A Charming Piece of Americana
That Never Existed . . .

Written and Illustrated by
Joan Berg Victor

FLAMBRO IMPORTS, INC.

First Edition

Published by Flambro Imports, Inc.
1260 Collier Rd., NW, Atlanta, Georgia 30318 USA
Library of Congress catalog card number: 91-090349
Printed in the United States of America

10 9 8 7 6 5 4 3 2 1

FOR ALLAN

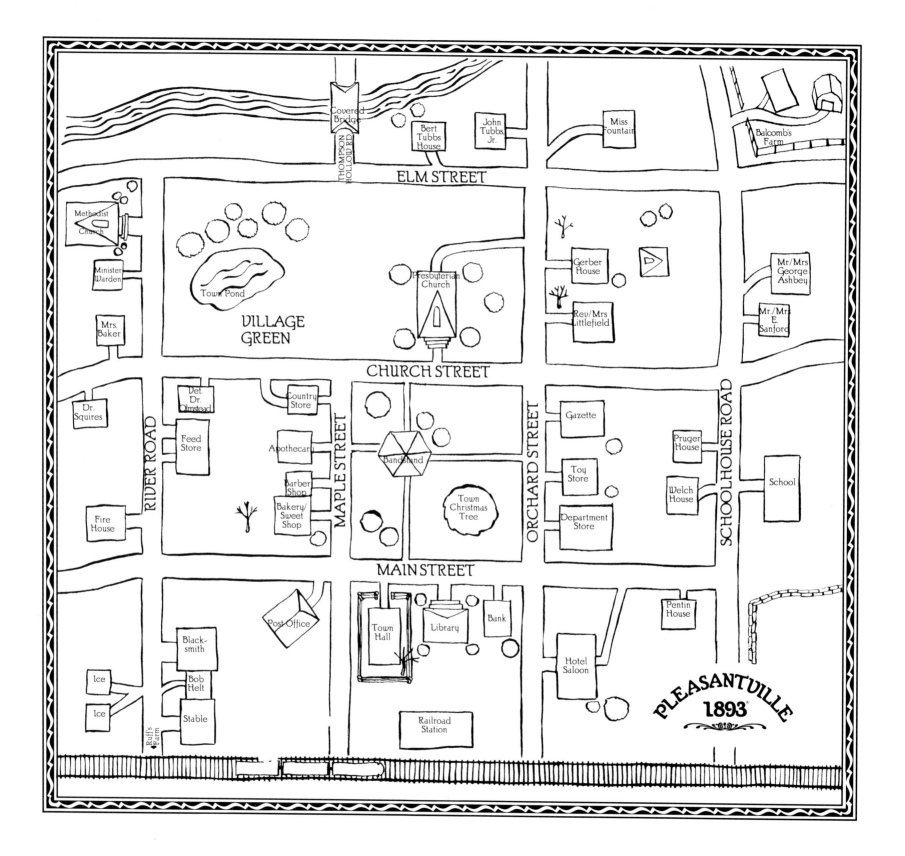

leasantville,
population 1173 in the year 1893, (this was an approximation as
little Elizabeth Grey and that sweet Roselynn Blancgard were both due to have babies any
day now ~ and it was rumored that Roselynn might be
having twins) ~ was situated just far enough away from any major
metropolis to think of itself as one of the major commercial
hubs in North America.

Pleasantville, the Monday before Christmas,
was caught in the worst storm that
has visited the town since the
memorable blizzard of 1884.
Snow began falling Monday
morning, continued all day
and through the night, and by
Tuesday morning there was a
total of eighteen inches of
snow.

Welcome to Pleasantville.

❦ Christmas is Coming ❦

The Town Square

In the year 1867, to celebrate their marriage, Gerhard and Mary Lou MacMurray donated the first Christmas tree to the town of Pleasantville. It was a twenty foot blue spruce and to hear the old folks tell, that tree was the prettiest Christmas tree the town ever saw.

As tradition would have it, every year on the first Saturday after Thanksgiving, the Pleasantville Christmas tree was placed in the same spot on the Town Square where the original MacMurray tree stood.

I guess you would describe the tree as a typical town Christmas tree - it seemed forever tall with a million lights on it. The theme changed each year, and this year the theme was gold, and almost all the ornaments on the tree were gold. Folks came from all over to see the Pleasantville tree - and they all agreed that it was, indeed, a very pretty tree - almost as pretty as the one way back in '67.

Mrs. Russell Warden and Mrs. Elizabeth Grey

When the tree went up in the Square, that signaled the rest of the town to begin their traditional decorating. Bob and Myrtle Ruff contributed the pine boughs from pine trees surrounding their farm to decorate the railings of the band stand. When they were finished, the Ruffs and Myrtle's brother Leonard and his new bride, Sis, were thanked profusely for the gorgeous job they did decorating.

On the Saturday evening before Christmas, every choral group in the town and a few from nearby towns: the high school chorus, the choirs from the town's churches, the Ladies Auxiliary singing group, and the Lions Club Barbershop Quartet, gathered at the Band Stand, received song sheets and candles and began a carolling tour of Pleasantville. At 10:30 p.m. the musical march ended. The candles were blown out, the song sheets were collected by Dehlia Robertson (to be used again next year) and all of the carollers filed into Reverend and Mrs. Littlefield's parlor for hot cocoa and cookies.

Clarke A. Sanford

E.L. O'Connor

❧ Pleasantville's Happenings ❧
in Black and White

The *Pleasantville Gazette*

The flourishing young town of Pleasantville never lacked for news, and , as in all growing towns, the citizens of Pleasantville wanted their own newspaper. After all you weren't an established town if you didn't have a newspaper.

The first newspaper, The Utilitarian, was published on July 7, 1863, by the late Orson B. Allaben. Mr. Allaben didn't know much about newspapers so, after struggling for many years to keep the paper going, he finally sold it on May 1, 1890 to W.E. Beals, an experienced newspaper man. Mr. Beals died suddenly in late 1890 and Mrs. Beals (who loved spreading news but had never been inside a newspaper plant) was left in charge.

Mrs. Beals desperately looked around for a buyer but she had no success until Clarke A. Sanford, who had spent two years as an editor in a neighboring town newspaper, came to Pleasantville to visit his Uncle Elmer and Aunt Dot Sanford. They were the proprietors of the Toy Store and Clarke's favorite relatives.

Clarke paid a visit to Mrs. Beals; they had tea and talked business. Mrs. Beals wanted $1400 for the newspaper and the plant, but Clarke had very little money. More desperate than ever, Mrs. Beals came up with an idea: she would take a note; if he made good, he'd have to pay the note; if he failed, she was in no worse position than she was now. The note was signed and the newspaper was turned over to Clarke A. Sanford around Christmastime, 1891 - and the *Pleasantville Gazette* made its debut in the form of a weekly news publication, appearing every Friday, rain or snow, covering major events and minor happenings.

Clarke A. Sanford

There were many difficulties for the young publisher. There was no money to pay the printers and bills were piling up. The paper earned $3.50 a week which went for Clarke's room and board. It seemed impossible to continue.

County Supervisor John Hitt came to the rescue. He went to the Board of Supervisors to tell them that the *Gazette* was near collapse and that Pleasantville badly needed to keep its newspaper. The Board granted the *Gazette* the printing of the Town Resolutions and the State Resolutions. This amounted to a sum of $1500. With that money, the *Gazette* was on its way.

Page 1. Column 1. *Pleasantville Gazette.* December 1, 1893

Daily Happenings for the Week

A Glimpse of the Life in a Busy
Country Village and the Little
Things That Make the Week's History

Taxes are due.
People are enjoying fine sleighing.
Ice harvest is full on and a fine quality is being harvested.
Local weather prophets predict 100 days of sleighing.
There were five wild geese wandering around the town pond.
Wild geese rarely stop hereabouts and it is thought that these five have strayed from their fellows.
It was a disgraceful row on Main Street Monday, when two drunken men (whose names will remain anonymous) quarreled all the way up through the village. They were too drunk to exchange blows but were not beyond the swearing point and their vile oaths and indecent language were heard a long way.

Mr. and Mrs. Billy Hendricks went to New York City on Tuesday where he will go into business.

The school closes on Friday, December 15, at Twelve O'Clock noon for the holiday vacation and will resume on Tuesday, January 2 1894.

The Classics Quartette gave a very pleasant entertainment at the Library Monday evening. Despite the blizzard, they were greeted by a well-filled house and hearty encores.

Miss Louise Baker is the guest of her sister, Mrs. Sam Gerber. Miss Baker has been in ill health and will remain here for a rest until after the holidays.

Page 2. *Pleasantville Gazette.* December 8, 1893

NEWS NOTES FROM ALL ABOUT

Pithy Paragraphs Pleasingly Penned

George Balcomb, owner of Balcomb Farm, killed a hog last Tuesday that dressed 561 pounds.

Samuel Baker, a Pleasantville resident and Mrs. Hannah B. Reed of Middletown, an attractive widow, were married in Pleasantville last Thursday morning. Reverend Littlefield of the Presbyterian Church officiated.

Horace Jenkins of Trout Creek, who died last week at the age of 98, was probably the oldest voter in the County. His first vote was cast for James Monroe and he had voted in every presidential election since.

Last Friday Doctor Squires of Pleasantville and nurse Miss Frieda Van Fuern performed an operation on Henry Sutter, owner and operator of Sutter Bros. Saloon, and removed a growth from his lower lip. The operation was entirely successful. Sutter Bros. Saloon remains open at its usual hours.

At Christmastime, the *Gazette* was so filled with advertisements that there was little space for news. As a way of saying "Thank you," Clarke Sanford published this editorial urging the townsfolk to support their local stores.

DO SHOPPING AT HOME
Local Merchants Have Everything You Want

—

Stores are Filled With Holiday Goods of the Best Quality and Prices are Right.

—

This is the particular time of the year when every person who gains a livelihood here should purchase every article needed either for Christmas gifts or general use from our local merchants. If local merchants do not have the things you desire, they will gladly procure them for you and at better bargains than you can secure out of town. The subject of trading at home is somewhat old fashioned, but by no means past usefulness.

In a village of our size we all are well wishers and friends; let us do our best to help each other along, even at a little sacrifice to ourselves if need be.

Trade at home.

—

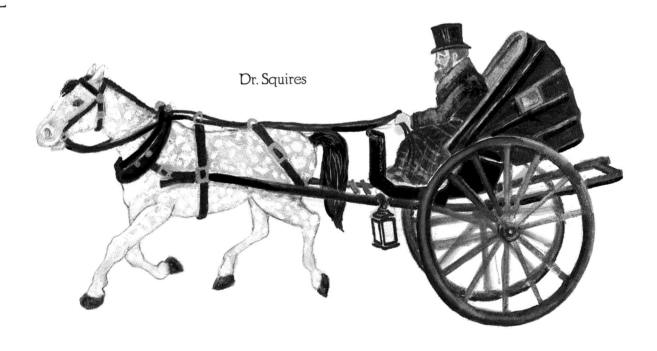

Dr. Squires

Mothers Be Careful of the health of your children. Look out for coughs, colds, croup, and whooping cough. Stop them in time ~ One Minute Cough Cure is the best remedy. Harmless and pleasant.
Sold by E.L. O'Connor, Apothecary.

—

A Pleasant Pill

No pill is as pleasant and positive as DeWitt's Little Early Risers. DeWitt's Little Early Risers are so mild and effective that children, delicate ladies and weak people enjoy their cleansing effect, while strong people say they are the best liver pills sold. Sold by E.L. O'Connor, Apothecary.

—

A Card

We, the undersigned, do hereby agree to refund the money on a 35¢ bottle of E. Green's Warranted Syrup of Tar if it fails to cure your cough or cold. Sold by E.L. O'Connor.

Page 3. *Pleasantville Gazette* December 8, 1893
A WEEK IN PLEASANTVILLE

Lights and Shadows Thrown on the Canvas of a Week

On Tuesday, while the freight train was going down the Trout Creek Grade and it neared the New Bridge, a brakestem broke, throwing one of the brakemen off the top of the car.

He was fortunate in falling in the snow, thus receiving only a few slight bruises besides a severe shaking up. He was not missed from the train until it reached Pleasantville.

—,—

In recognition of the faithful services of Carl Olmsted, mail carrier between Pleasantville and the outlying areas, his friends along the route have kindly gotten together and presented him with a fur overcoat, a nice robe and a cap, the total cost of which was over $9.25.

Until our Pleasantville Post Office is finally completed, hopefully by early next year, mail will be distributed from the residence of Mr. and Mrs. George Hendricks.

Page 4. *Pleasantville Gazette.* December 8, 1893

ON THE SICK LIST

Those who are ill in the territory of
the *Pleasantville Gazette*

Carl Gerber is confined to the house with measles. William Todd, better known as Shorty Todd who has been on the sick list of late, is some better. Mrs. L.J. Tompkins is very sick, with but little hopes of her recovery. Sadie Baker has been under the doctor's care and is somewhat improved. There has been a general epidemic of tonsillitis here of late but all are reported better.

✤ A God-Fearing People ✤

Reverend Littlefield posted a notice in the lobby of the Pleasantville Presbyterian Church and sent a copy of the notice to the *Gazette*. "Christmas giving: there will be many dollars spent this Christmas for gifts that carry no long-lasting nor practical value whatever. A gift to the Lord at this season is most fitting. Search your hearts and give what is most appropriate to your means.

"Show your love of the Lord by giving a gift to your church.

"Bible study classes will meet on Wednesday evenings at 7 p.m.

On Friday evening, the twenty-second of December, a general frolic will be given for the children, in the basement of the church, beginning at 5:30 and lasting one hour. The Christmas pageant will be put on by the Sunday School and all fourteen of our children will perform. The theme of this year's pageant is Noah and the flood.

"On Saturday evening, the twenty-third of December, at 7:30 p.m. a short program will be rendered in the main room, followed by carolling. Carollers will gather, as usual, at the band stand in the town square. "Christmas religious services begin at 8:00 p.m. Christmas Eve with Christmas Eve candlelight services. Come early to avoid the throngs of enthusiastic worshippers.

"Mrs. Littlefield joins me in wishing all of our beloved townspeople a joyous God-filled Holiday Season."

Signed,

Rev. Edwin Littlefield

❧ The Pleasantville Presbyterian Church ❧

The Pleasantville Presbyterian Church faced west directly across the town square from the bank and library. It was a beautiful gothic structure, with two-story windows, three-story high interior and a balcony with a highly polished oak railing. It was the pride of the entire church family.

The minister, Edwin Littlefield, was a pious and almost cheerful man who had a way of always being there when he was needed. His wife, Emily, was her husband's ever-ready helpmate. She was sober (and expected everyone else to be the same), stern and devout.

Two weeks before Christmas, Flower Chairman Celly Hartshone gathered a group of women who were delighted to be asked to serve on Celly's committee. With the aid of Sexton Wooten, (a tall, gangly man who had an angelic smile), it was their task to decorate the church with greens and red ribbons.

A work party was arranged by Celly the following Saturday evening to put up the decorations. Mrs. Heley made fruit punch and that saintly lady, Freida Van Fuern, who always did everything that needed doing, baked pecan sandies.

Perhaps it was the spiked punch, perhaps it was just an over zealous leap of faith, but by evening's end, the green boughs and red ribbons were covered with tinsel.

Emily, the minister's wife lost her composure. But as she was searching for the proper way to reprimand the committee, she seemed to be taken over, and quite divinely she uttered, "We Christians are a simple lot and never showy, but, well, it does add a bit to our joyous occasion."

Thus a new tradition was born in Pleasantville.

❧ Reverend Littlefield's House ❧

Reverend Edwin Littlefield and his wife Emily, and their two boys, Glen and Oswald, lived in the large brick house to the right of the Pleasantville Presbyterian Church on the corner of Orchard and Church Streets.

It was a great treat to be invited to the minister's house for tea on Sunday afternoon. Tea was served in the parlor—a room which was used only on special occasions. The walls were covered with large oil paintings of family members. In the center of the room was a lace covered round table upon which sat the large family Bible. In it were inscribed all of the family records.

Everyone donned his or her Sunday best and his or her very best manners, and chatted in low tones about such topics as the weather, the latest marriages and births. They very politely sipped tea (cider for the children) and ate Emily's sugar cookies and jelly squares.

This notice appeared in the "This Week's Happenings" column in the December 15, 1893 *Gazette.*

Notes from the Pleasantville Methodist Church:

All are invited to attend the pre-holiday religious studies group on Tuesday evening at 7:30 p.m.

As is our annual custom, parishioners are invited at that time to place their presents to our Lord and to the Methodist Church on the Christmas tree in the lobby of the church.

The choir is in fine voice, having practiced for some time now some excellent Christmas music which will be rendered at both the morning and evening services. Hymns Nos. 107-112, 113, 115, 123, and 124, and other joyous songs will be heard.

If, at no other time of the year, we go to the Lord's House, let us be sure to go at this glad season, and let us go with joy and generosity in our hearts. There is room for all. Be sure to come.

The Sunday school will convene at 11:30 a.m. Let not a Christian stay away nor be tardy at this season.

After the holidays, the Tuesday evening religious studies class will host A. Adam Hudgins, former registrar at the State Prison. He will speak on 'Religion in Prisons.' Mr. Hudgins will tell of many interesting experiences.

Ken Brown

❦ The Pleasantville Methodist Church ❦

The First Methodist Church of Pleasantville was built in 1850 and stood on the corner of Church and Maple Streets. The original building still exists but when the new church was erected, the old one was moved behind the Gerber house (no one knew why exactly; maybe because no one knew quite what to do with it, so Sam Gerber said, "Might as well put it behind my house. I've got plenty of room."). It was eventually used as a club house for the Boy Scouts.

In 1880, the new Methodist Church was built on the corner of River Road and Elm Street, in sight of the town pond, with Minister and Mrs. Russell Warden leading the congregation. Minister Warden was an extremely enthusiastic young preacher who, whenever he spotted four or more souls gathered, would take it as an opportunity to preach.

The new church was nothing fancy; in fact, the interior was quite plain. It accommodated two hundred worshippers comfortably, with an impressive oak stand in the front of the altar, that doubled as a pulpit and lectern. But the most important object in the new church was the harmonium which was bought with a donation from Sadie Baker, in the name of her dear departed husband Harold. It stood prominently to the left of the oak stand.

When one thinks of the Pleasantville Methodist Church, he or she recalls the church bells at Christmas time. They sounded throughout the town and beyond, into the country-side ~ as far as Balcomb's farm.

❧ Dwellings ❧

The Gerber House, *or* ...
The House with the Church Behind It

Sam Gerber lived in the blue-grey house on Orchard Street, just off the town square. He lived there with his wife, Rose (his childhood sweetheart), his two sons, Toddy and Carl, an old Coon cat named Harry, and a hunting hound called Skip.

The house had been in the family for three generations and almost every activity which took place in the house was a continuation of some family tradition. The seasons were marked by a change in the breakfast menu: blueberry muffins appeared and it had to be summer; Burt Tubbs' honey was set on the table and the family knew summer was winding down. Cold or snow, it wasn't winter until Rose's porridge and molasses greeted the morning.

The house wasn't heated well and one could catch cold if one wasn't careful. So winter bathtime became another ritual in the Gerber household: every Saturday night, the galvanized tub was set in front of the coal stove and Carl and Toddy took their baths. After the boys fell asleep, Rose and Sam had their baths.

And Christmas was no exception to family tradition. The first Sunday in December, the Christmas rituals began with a carriage ride or sleigh ride (depending upon the weather) out to Ruff's farm to cut a Christmas tree. Then the tree trimming – each family member had an annual task. One year, Toddy was sick in bed, and Carl got to do his big brother's favorite task of setting up the trains around the base of the tree. Toddy didn't speak to Carl for almost two weeks.

Miss Fountain's House, or ...
The House with the Red Roof

A sign of the times was when the Pleasantville Hotel opened its doors to the public in 1885. But even though the new hotel was thriving, Miss Fountain's boarding house continued to bring in paying guests. City folks came and spent a week at Christmas, and two weeks, or perhaps a month in the summer.

The boarding house was situated on the road heading out of town, a quarter of a mile from the town square. Miss Fountain came from the city and she would tell her guests that she had been educated in London, England in the arts. And artistic she was: every painting, every object in the house was precisely placed, never to be moved unless by her direction.

Young Leonard Finch, Junior (Sis and Leonard's son) started working at Miss Fountain's when he was sixteen. He left school that year because at sixteen years, he was expected to help out with the family expenses. Leonard Jr. worked for a dollar a week. Miss Fountain told him he could have tips, but that only came to about thirty-five cents a week. A special holiday week might bring him fifty cents. The money he earned went directly to his father.

Miss Fountain had an ice house out in back and Fred Clutt came once a week to bring ice. She never understood how he managed to arrive just as supper was being served, and however reluctant he was, he always managed to stay for supper, a smoke, and a game of dominoes.

The House of Mr. and Mrs. John Tubbs, Jr. or The Yellow House on Orchard Street

"You must see this fair" - The World's Columbian Exposition was the marvel of technological progress, and John and Clarissa Tubbs meant to see it. As the *Pleasantville Gazette* stated on page 4: "Mr. and Mrs. John Tubbs, Jr. journeyed to Chicago on the overnight train to visit the Columbian Exposition. They returned one week later with a machine that could sing and play."

It was the first Edison phonograph to come to Pleasantville, and it stood in a place of honor in the Tubbs' parlor. Neighbors would pay a visit on Saturday evenings and sit listening in delighted disbelief to the sounds coming from that wondrous machine.

There was one additional treasure which Clarissa and John brought home from the Exposition: a stereoscopic viewer or, what most folks called a stereoscope, together with three or four sets of pictures.

The children, Glen and Margaret, were delighted. Looking through the stereoscope they giggled at pictures of children imitating grownups. Although John was rather disdainful at first, he too became fascinated by the stereoscope and it soon became the mainstay of the family entertainment.

It should be mentioned that the Tubbs, Jr. home on Orchard Street was Pleasantville's one example of Neo-Classical architecture. The cost of the house, not including mantels and heater was $2500 in the year 1890.

❧ Commerce ❧

The Toy Store

Facing the town square, next door to the Department
Store, on Orchard Street, was Dot and Elmer
Sanford's Toy Store.

Every year, for the past twelve years, after the first
big snowfall, Mr. S. (as he was known in town) and
the two Sanford boys, Thomas and Will, built a
snowman right next to the store. Mr. S had, a few
years back, contributed his favorite red and white striped scarf to
the snowman and Dot Sanford's Dad, Grandpa Sam had been
pressured to donate his old bowler hat. That handsome snowman
stood next to the Toy Store until the late February thaw.

The Sanford's Toy Store was the fulfillment of every child's fantasy:
there were shelves and shelves of dolls and wagons and balls and
games; there were ice skates and jars of marbles and bubble
pipes, spinning tops and wind-up tin soldiers. There was a large
red satin-covered box sitting next to the cash register where all
children were instructed to place their letters to Santa Claus. A
week before Christmas, Mr. and Mrs. Sanford made a point of
letting every parent and grandparent in on those secrets.

One of Pleasantville's famous landmarks was the dapple-grey
wooden rocking horse standing just inside the entrance to the
Toy Store. One could not enter the store without, depending upon
one's age or state of mind, patting the horse on the nose or
yanking its scraggly tail.

The Sweet Shoppe & Bakery

The Sweet Shoppe was the place to come to find out what was going on in town.

Charlie Hubbard was 36 when he opened his doors for business. He was skinny as a rail, but as the years in the Bakery added up, so did the pounds and Charlie became his own best advertisement.

Rumor has it that he won his dear wife Jeanette's heart with his divinity fudge - his own secret recipe. When she finally said "Yes," Charlie thought it fitting to have the wedding reception in the Sweet Shoppe. The entire town came, except Dot Sanford, who was sick in bed with the grippe.

As Christmas time neared in Pleasantville, amazing goodies appeared: gingerbread boys and girls 12 inches tall, big white puffs of air and marshmallow with candied fruits in the center, sugar cookies in the shape of stars, moons, angels, and trees. Christmas Eve, as everyone was heading home, they made a brief stop to say "Merry Christmas" to Charlie and Jeanette and shared the last remaining holiday sweets.

The Department Store

This sign appeared in the window of the Department Store:
"The store of Christmas Gifts for All. The cheery holiday spirit prevades here. Useful gifts too numerous to mention. A gift item for every member of your family, every friend and everyone for whose pleasure you are planning."

Directly across the town square from the bakery, John Tubbs and his son, John, Jr., maintained the Pleasantville Department Store. John's father, Burt, came to Pleasantville fifty-five years ago in a horse-drawn wagon, piled high with woolens and calicoes, yarn and thread, spices and pots, and a variety of cooking utensils. He eventually outgrew his store on wheels and bought the property on the corner of Main and Orchard Streets. Together with his son John, Burt Tubbs opened The Pleasantville Department Store to the public on September 19, 1858.

Burt had the foresight to see that Pleasantville would grow to become the hub of the county, where folks would come from far and wide to buy everything they could not produce themselves. John's son, John Jr. came to work in the store in 1891 and the following year, his grandfather, Burt, retired. "The store's in good hands," Burt said. "Now it's time for me to tend to my bees, do a little hunting and fishing and spend a little time with my dear wife."

28

❧ A Couple of Items of Interest ❧

A Strange Accident Takes Place

This article appeared at the bottom of page 3
Pleasantville Gazette, December 15, 1893

On Wednesday, Doctor Squires, our town physician, was summoned to the farm of George and Carolyn Miller. There was an unusual accident early that evening when a cow fell on Mrs. Miller.

From what we can ascertain, Mrs. Miller had been milking the cows and was about to finish the last cow when Mr. Miller proceeded to give the cows their hay. The cow she was milking reached out for some hay and in doing so, slid and fell, resting entirely on Mrs. Miller. She was immediately freed from her unhealthy position and carried to the house where it was observed that she was miraculously alive, and according to Doctor Squires, "Just fine."

Married the "Hired Girl"

On page 4 of the same issue of the *Gazette* the following item of interest appeared

Doctor Louis Haltendorf, a young Cincinnati physician who recently took up residence in Pleasantville, eloped with Pearl Simpson, the domestic employed at his father's house. The young doctor went to Detroit to marry the girl to avoid his sister with aristocratic tastes.

"I shall never get over it," wailed sister Elizabeth when she heard of the marriage. Perhaps not. Her case is chronic. But what of Pearl Simpson? In the first place the young physician was deeply in love with her, and as he is a young fellow of discriminating tastes, it may be taken for granted that the girl is worthy. She has a trim figure, a very sweet disposition and is a cook and caterer *par excellence*; just the sort of girl to make an excellent wife. The doctor's father philosophically remarked when he was told of the marriage, "Well, he might have done worse."

Of course he might—had he possessed less heart and less good sense. He married his Pearl and at the same time dealt a body blow at snobbery and American class distinctions.

Long life and happiness to Doctor Haltendorf and his precious Pearl.

❧ Miss Josephine ❧
and
The Pleasantville Library

Around 1873 or 1874, a one-room library was opened on the second floor of the building that now houses Burt and John Tubbs' Department Store. Carrie Russell, Frank's widow (he was the teacher in the old log schoolhouse), was helpful in collecting books, setting up the library, and then acting as Pleasantville's first librarian.

As Pleasantville grew and prospered, the town's elders felt there was a need for a more impressive monument to culture and civilization in the form of a new library - an imposing Neo Gothic structure of red brick with limestone columns. Josephine Littlefield, oldest sister of the Reverend Littlefield, was a college graduate and a woman full of Christian virtue and wisdom, and the obvious choice for Librarian.

As librarian, Miss Josephine's entire week centered around two events: the Saturday afternoon story hour, which was held every Saturday afternoon from the second Saturday in September to the third Saturday in April; and Doctor Squires' Wednesday morning visits to the Library.

Josephine had secretly adored Doctor Squires since they met on his first Wednesday visit a year after his wife had passed. Her greatest delight was selecting books she had loved reading - they seemed to enjoy the same kinds of books - and present them to him for his reading pleasure. The books would be waiting in a little stack on the corner of her desk, with a carefully penned note: "For Doctor Squires, to fill one's leisure hours with the joys and benefits of good books. Signed, Josephine L."

Doctor Squires would greet Josephine with a sweeping gesture of removing his hat and bowing deeply. She, in turn, would blush and place her fingers to her lips to conceal a slight giggle.

On the Saturday after Thanksgiving, when Pleasantville officially began the holiday season, Santa greeted the town's children at the entrance to the Library. Christmas books and periodicals filled the display cases and old Christmas cards were strung in boughs around the entrance hall. If the weather were warm, Santa would greet the boys and girls in the town square across from the Library; if the day were cold, with rain or snow, Santa moved indoors. Miss Josephine and the Library committee passed out cider and cookies and sheets of paper listing all of the books to be read at the Saturday story hour throughout the year.

In her holiday bulletin, posted in the lobby of the Library, Miss Josephine offered advice to the town's adults and children for vacation time:

"I can offer you no better advice for the winter holiday than
1. to read a good book
2. to do a kind deed
3. to do some form of beneficial exercise

"The pleasures and benefits of a good book are beyond measure. Mind you, I cannot, in expression of my wish, send you each a good book (I should have to be a millionaire in order to do that). But I am able to tell you to come to the Library, and by doing so, I am making my wish practical.

"I am deeply disappointed to announce that the New World Glee Club became snowbound and was unable to keep their Thursday evening engagement."

❧ Our Town Heroes ❧

Fire House

Since a fire was the most feared happening, the Pleasantville fire fighters were considered the heroes of the town.

George Hendricks

Cecil Polley was the first chief of the Pleasantville Volunteer Fire Department. His full-time job was that of village street cleaner. When he retired, George Hendricks became the chief.

When the bugle sounded at the fire house, everyone stopped and listened; the volunteer firemen stopped whatever they were doing, and rushed to the fire house. The fire horses—Ole Sam and Barney—were already hitched to the steam pumper, ready to go. When the men were gathered, several jumped onto the fire engine. Those who came late had to run to catch up. Young boys chased the fire truck until they were out of breath and sat down on the side of the street to await the fire truck's return.

There was a Volunteer Women's Auxiliary of the fire department, made up of the wives of the fire fighters. They met once a year to choose committees. There was the fire committee headed by Cornelia Polley, wife of the retired fire chief Cecil Polley, that was responsible for bringing coffee and sandwiches and sweet buns to the firemen while they fought fires; there was the breakfast committee which four times a year would hold fund raising breakfasts to raise money for fire fighting equipment.

The breakfasts were held at the fire hall and the fire engine was moved out onto the street to make room for the crowd. It was a great social event. Everyone would come to show their support and to eat unlimited pancakes and eggs, ham and sausage and biscuits and coffee. Bob Taylor sang his country songs and was accompanied by young Kevin Ballard (his ancestors were some of the first settlers in these parts) playing the fiddle. The breakfasts began after church and lasted until sundown.

❧ A House of Learning ❧

If you were to cross the Village Green, walk past the pond, and bear left on Elm Street you'd see the old log schoolhouse. The last teacher to teach in that building was Frank Russell. Billy Russell, his grandson, is the principal of the new Pleasantville School.

Pleasantville was a farm community and youngsters were needed on the farm. After all, when it came time to work, you worked; school was secondary. With all the time taken out for work, some of the students were 23 or 24 years old when they finally finished high school. Summer was the time to plant and all hands were needed. So, in the late spring and summer, few boys attended school. As time passed and more boys wished to stay in school, the idea of summer vacation was created.

When the old log school burned down, the town moved the school into the fire hall and finally, in 1890, the students moved into the newly-built school on Schoolhouse Road.

The youngsters walked to school and walked home. If it was ten below zero, they still walked. As the town grew and spread out, Lester LePuis began to pick up the students and bring them to school in his horse-drawn cart or, in winter, his horse-drawn sleigh.

The first and second grades were taught by Miss Zena Warden, sister of the young minister of the Methodist Church and a recent arrival in town.

May McCadden taught third and fourth grades. She had taught for years. The children called her a strict teacher, but she taught well and knew how to handle the youngsters.

The janitor at the school was Leslie Demont. When he finished his daily chores at the school, Mr. D (as he was known), had a second and very important job. Every evening at exactly six, he left the school with a step ladder and a gallon of kerosene, and walked through the town lighting all of the streetlamps.

❧ Fire at the Hotel ❧

Pleasantville Gazette, December 15, 1893

Townsfolk looked on with intense excitement last Wednesday evening as they witnessed the fire burning in the chimney of the Pleasantville Hotel. Flames could be seen from as far away as Ruff's farm as they burst fiercely from the tall chimney and sent sparks spraying down on the roof and onto the people standing in the street. Happily, the roof was covered with snow so the hotel itself was spared from the fire.

The fire department hastened to the scene and put out the blaze. Cornelia Polley and her Ladies' Auxiliary served coffee and cinnamon buns to our loyal fire fighters.

Page 3 - *Pleasantville Gazette*, December 22, 1893

"Christmas dinner will be served in the dining room of the Pleasantville Hotel, in spite of the chimney fire, on Saturday afternoon at One O'clock p.m. at regular rates.

"Patrons wishing dinner are asked to make reservations not later than Friday afternoon."

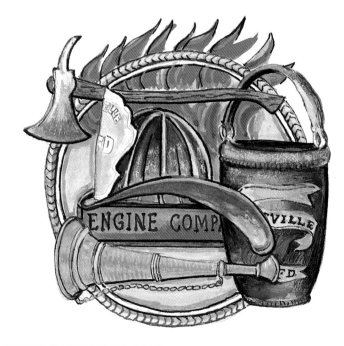

❧ Mason's Hotel & Saloon ❧

Clyde and Clara Ashbey

The famous Mason's Hotel in Pleasantville was on the corner of Main and Orchard Streets, directly across the street from the department store. It had three floors and a basement and was the pride of the townfolk. The hotel was quite an impressive building with an elegant lobby and a large ballroom in the back, and Henry Sutter's Saloon was on the left as you walked in.

Henry Sutter, it was frequently recalled, was the town youth who, on a dare at the age of eleven, shinnied up the old town flag pole and couldn't figure out how to come down. After some time passed and the sun was soon to set, the town fire company was called and worked until way after dark and vowed never to come to his rescue again.

Henry opened the Sutter Bros. Saloon (an odd name, as he was an only child) in 1883 to the pleasure of the townsmen and the chagrin of the townswomen. It was open six days and seven nights a week, serving lunch Monday - Saturday. The lunch time menu varied: Tuesday, Thursday, and Saturday: hot brisket sandwich for 15¢; corned beef on German rye bread for 20¢ on Monday, Wednesday and Friday. Clearly, no one frequented the saloon for the sake of the food.

The hotel was started by Mr. and Mrs. George Ashbey, the late parents of Clyde Ashbey, who runs the hotel today. The name Mason was Mrs. Ashbey's maiden name.

Every Christmas Day since the hotel doors opened, the Ashbey family welcomed all the townsfolk to gather in the hotel lobby for a cup of egg nog and Charlie Hubbard's fruit cake and plum pudding.

❧ A Romance ❧

Our Hero

The following article appeared in the
Pleasantville Gazette on February 17, 1893:

"Last Sunday, a young man who has been working on Balcomb's farm hired a horse and sleigh from the village smithy. He and his young lady companion went for a sleigh ride in the countryside. Everything went happily until, as the sleigh climbed a snow drift, it tipped over and dumped its occupants into the snow. The horse became frightened and took off across the fields, finally to be stopped by local blacksmith, Bob Helt, and his mare, near the skating pond. The young people made their way back to town on foot, safe but quite chilled."

Miss May McCadden, while reading her weekly Gazette, spotted this notice and it not only caught her eye but caught hold of her heart and made the beat quicken.

Meantime, behind the soon-to-be-finished Post Office were two buildings; the Livery and the Blacksmith Shop ~ two separate buildings (in case of fire) attached by the rooms Bob Helt lived in.

The fire in the forge went down but it never went out. The town blacksmith or "Village Smithy" as he was called, was Bob Helt. He wasn't just a horse shoer, he was a FARRIER, he proudly declared (no one quite knew the distinction between the two). He shod horses, repaired wagon wheels, he could do any kind of iron work required by the Pleasantville townsfolk. Mr. Helt rented wagons, sleighs, horses. He also boarded horses (Dr. Squires kept his horse with Mr. Helt).

"There are all kinds of ways to shoe a horse," he would tell in a pausing, slow, carefully thinking manner of speech, "a farrier makes a particular shoe for each horse; I call it 'corrective shoeing.' I know what to do when I see a horse with a problem."

Blacksmithing had been his life for as long as anyone could remember. As a boy, he hung around the local smithy, Mr. Garrison, and when he turned thirteen, he began his apprenticeship.

The piece of work he was most proud of was the ornate iron fence for the Methodist Church: its curves and swirls and the way in which all the strips of iron met in perfect points.

Nobody knew much about Bob Helt. They knew he lived alone in the attached rooms between the blacksmith and livery shops, he never married, he never went calling. He once told Doc Squires (while they shared a mug of Bob's homemade wine) that he had been disappointed early in his life and "... I just never bothered after that."

"I had a pure bred Morgan, a combination saddle and driving horse, that I went to New Hampshire to get; she was a mare named Maizie, and I had my dog, a Springer Spaniel named C.C. I'd ride the mare around the hills outside town every Sunday and then, go to Sunday dinner at the hotel."

In the fall, he would make homemade wine - a favorite of Doc Squires and several of the other men in town. While Bob and the Doc sat around sampling the season's brew, Bob would tell his stories, like the time he was grooming the Doc's horse, "The horse got a bee on her belly ... she got stung and I got kicked."

No one was in the shop that Saturday when Miss May McCadden, the third and fourth grade school teacher, entered the blacksmith shop to hire a carriage. "Good Day," she almost whispered, and then went on to explain that she wanted to show her sister, June (May McCadden was born, of course, in May and her younger sister, June, two Junes later), the countryside and the changing leaves.

May McCadden suddenly realized that she had been rattling on and she put her gloved hand to her mouth. But Bob Helt had barely glanced up as he began to ready a rig. May McCadden was hardly pretty, yet she wasn't homely. She was a couple of years past thirty, sober and intelligent, and to Bob Helt's mind and ear, she possessed a sweet, musical speaking voice.

As she climbed up into the seat of the carriage, with the blacksmith's awkward and formal aid, May McCadden asked, "Would you like to come and have tea while my sister is visiting?" (She simply could not believe that she said that.)

Bob Helt, at first, thought she must be speaking to someone else, but he looked around and no one else was present. He must have misunderstood what she had said. May's courage kept up, and she repeated, "We would be pleased if you cared to join us for tea." He was speechless. He knew that she was waiting for him to respond and he did not know what to say. She was still waiting, and he still did not know what to say. He had no proper suit of clothes, he wouldn't know what to talk about.

Was she making fun of him? At last he spoke, "I thank you for your invitation, but I do not go visiting very often."

On Sunday, when he rode his mare out into the countryside, Bob Helt felt strange and his head was filled with confusion. He was suspicious. Yep, she probably was making fun of him. After all, he thought, without being very social, people usually don't go looking you up. He rode along, unable to get it out of his mind. Things never are as they seem, he thought; people like me are shy or suspicious, but never as unsocial as they appear.

Still, he couldn't help but be curious. He regretted turning her down. He'd done that a lot in his life. Don't say anything if you don't know what to say. Now he'd have to find some excuse.

Bob rode aimlessly, pondering the situation. "Since she doesn't own a horse and wagon, I'll have to look for another approach—something ... so I can have an excuse to get over there.

"She boards with Mrs. Murphy. Mrs. Murphy has a wagon ... maybe some iron work ... of course, her wood stove. That's it."

He found himself going down town more often than was usual. Finally, maybe a week or so passed and he saw Mrs. Murphy in front of the bank. They greeted each other and somehow Bob Helt reminded her,
"Devious devil," he thought. He blushed and slightly smiled. "Oh, yes," she remembered, "the wood stove in the parlor is cracked."

"We have to do this on a Saturday," (so we make sure May M. is at home), "only because I can't leave the shop during the week." Bob couldn't believe what he had done.

Saturday comes and Bob finds himself in Mrs. Murphy's parlor, repairing the crack in the stove, and stretching it out for all its worth. Now, lo and behold, it comes into noon and dinnertime, and Mrs. Murphy invites him to stay for dinner.

Mrs. Murphy calls to May to come for dinner. "Dear thing, she seldom comes to dinner," but she comes down and is already seated when Bob comes in. He washes his hands in the sink. Hoping no one will notice, he takes a little water and slicks his hair back, and is seated.

There he is seated across the table from May McCadden, head down, looking at the table. He's created the situation and now he is so embarrassed he cannot speak. Mrs. Murphy begins to get the idea. "I got to say something," he thinks. "Ask her something." "Did you and your sister enjoy the countryside?" She did.

Mrs. Murphy leaves the table to get something.

"Would you like to go out and look at the leaves again?"

"I think I would like to do that very much," May replies.

Bob and May do go riding, and while looking at the leaves, they get to talking about horses. When she was young, May's family had horses. Bob finds an excuse to go somewhere else the following Sunday. He invites May to the Fair. They race horses at the Fair. They go and have a fine time.

Then something surprising happened. Bob started staying away, avoiding May McCadden. He got busy on weekends. When he saw May on the street, he would greet her and exchange pleasantries, but he avoided any extended conversation.

He worried over it and was upset about it but wasn't able to do anything about it. He wanted something to happen but was afraid for it to happen. May would have to be the one to break the ice.

Time passes and one Saturday in November, May McCadden comes to the shop and finding him alone, she takes a deep breath and says, "I can see it is obvious you are avoiding my company. I thought you and I were good company together and suddenly, everything stopped and I want to know why."

"She's got courage, this girl," Bob thought. "She must have to, to be a school teacher and put up with all those little ruffians. No tears —if she were a cry-baby, I'd have no interest. She looks a little nervous ; so am I."

She stood there waiting for a reply. And Bob stood there, facing her, trying to sort out all the thoughts racing through his head. He began … slowly at first, then gaining courage:

"Why I got a little nervous because, well, I think I got nervous to get too close to somebody." He thought he was making no sense. "I got a little nervous because I started to care for you. I kind of regretted it … I mean, the nervousness … but I didn't know what to do about it." He paused, it seemed like a very long time. Then he continued:

"I'd like to pick up where we left off."

And they did. Bob Helt escorted May home. "I will be calling on you real soon."

Two weeks before Christmas, Sunday, December 10, to be exact, Bob and May had been out for a sleigh ride and they stopped at the covered bridge out past Balcomb's farm.

"You've noticed, May, that I've been spending a lot of time at Mrs. Murphy's house ..." This was his way of leading up to what he wanted to say. "I can't keep imposing on Mrs. Murphy." Silence ... for what seemed like a long time.

"We might as well get married and you can come and live with me and that would solve all the running back and forth and imposing. Besides," he added, "that way you wouldn't have to rent a horse and wagon, you'd have one of your own."

I'm not certain he even waited for a reply, he just went on. "If you accept, then it's all settled. We'll be married on December 18, a week from Monday."

Bob stepped back, as if he had to rethink something. Then he went on.

"Now I don't want to misrepresent myself; I can't afford to keep a woman that isn't working. I realize married ladies are not permitted to teach school, but I have only two rooms. That wouldn't keep you busy all day."

May was finally able to speak.

"I'm not the kind of person to sit home, besides which I was thinking," (one almost got the impression that May had known all this was coming), "the post office will soon be ready and perhaps, I could work there. After all, it's just next door and I could be close by to make supper and help out in the shop."

It was settled, and each of them, in his or her own way, was pleased as punch. He drove her home in an awkward, almost embarrassed silence, a silence which was periodically broken with Bob clearing his throat and commenting on the day, the weather, the horse. May would agree and they would resume their silence.

❧ A Portrait ❧

The Ice Man

Fred Clutt was the ice man in the 1880s and 90s. He lived alone in a small apartment over the Department Store. He built two ice houses between the Post Office and the railroad tracks.

Back in those times, folks didn't have any coolers. In the coldest part of the winter, Fred hired a wagon driver (one of the fellows who worked at Ruff's farm during the summer) and they cut ice in the Halcottsville Pond (just outside of town). The ice was between six and fifteen inches thick. They sawed the ice by hand, into cakes eighteen by twenty-four inches, and loaded them onto the wagon to be carried to the ice houses. After the ice was stacked, hay was laid on top to act as insulation.

When winter was over, Fred would push his wheelbarrow up and down the town streets, all around the square—that wheelbarrow squeaked very loudly delivering ice to the stores and the houses in town, at the cost of two or three cents a cake.

❧ Progress ❧

The Valley and Mountain Railroad

This notice appeared in the *Pleasantville Gazette*, December 8, 1893:
   "The V & M snow plow was used last Monday and Tuesday to
clear the tracks of snow and all trains were on schedule time."
Station Master W. Pattberg

   Beginning in the 1880s, there was a craze to build
railroads. Every town wanted the train, and Pleasantville
was no exception. There were no roads to speak
of—just mud and ruts. There were few stage coaches.
If a person wanted to get somewhere, he or she
walked or went by horse.
   Finally, beginning in the fall of 1886, the train
came through Pleasantville. First, it came once a
week, and later, three times a week. It was the
highlight of each of these days and townsfolk
hurried down to the station to meet the train: to see
who got on the train, and who got off; who was
leaving town and who was coming in. They wanted
to see what their neighbors had ordered from the
mail order catalogues.
   Walt Pattberg was the Station Master. His official
tasks were: sweeping out the station, selling tickets,
making certain that the orders were handed up to the
engineers on the trains, and stopping road traffic when
trains came through town.

Later on, as Pleasantville got a little busier and Walt Pattberg got a little older, Norman Sanford became the crossing guard. He'd boldly strut into the middle of the road, thrust one arm into the air while the other hand planted a pole, on top of which was a sign: "Railroad Crossing - STOP."

Two weeks before Christmas, the scheduled Tuesday train arrived as usual. Folks got off the train; others got on. Boxes and crates were unloaded. Those expecting packages eagerly searched for his or her parcel. The curious onlookers observed and, of course, would take away many tales to tell over tea at the counter in O'Connor's Pharmacy.

When all the packages had been claimed, a single box remained: a rather large parcel wrapped in heavy brown paper, tied with yards and yards of twine, and surrounding an exquisitely penned address, were glued many exotic looking stamps.

Miss Frieda Van Fuern
Pleasantville

Walt Pattberg spotted Mark Balcomb dawdling near the entrance to the station.

"Go to Doc Squires' office and tell Miss Van Fuern that there's a very important looking package with her name on it."

A very few minutes passed before Mark returned with Frieda Van Fuern who was quite taken aback by this mysterious parcel.

"Mark, may I trouble you to carry this for me?"

"Gladly, Miss Van Fuern."

In silence, they walked; Mark, a little behind Miss Van Fuern, until they reached Mrs. Sadie Baker's small white house on the corner of River Road and Church Street. Here, on the second floor, Frieda rented a room.

Mark carried the box into the front hall and set it down on the rose-colored Oriental rug.

"Thank you, Mark. You are a dear young man. Be certain to send my respects to your fine parents."

"Anytime I can be of help, Miss Van Fuern. 'Bye."

Frieda gazed at the package. It came from her family in Bavaria. Her eyes filled with tears, her heart was beating very rapidly. She dared not lift this wonderful box, for fear of dropping it. She straightened herself, took a deep breath and stooped down and picked up the box. Ever so carefully she made her way up the stairs to her room.

Frieda set the box upon her bed. She ran her fingers over the writing. She touched the stamps. She smiled; for a moment she was home in Munich. Her Mother was there, and her Father and Grandmother.

She unknotted the twine, unfolded the brown wrapping and removed the lid. Between the packing, she discovered a glass ball, then another. There were other glass ornaments: a bell, a Saint Nicholas, and there were two glass birds with tails made of real feathers. She reached down into the box to be certain she had found all the treasures.

Wait. There was something else in the box. She lifted out a gold foil-wrapped object. Frieda felt the wrapping, trying to imagine what it contained.

She delicately opened the wrapping.

"Oh. It's beautiful. A nutcracker … Grandmama sent me her treasured nutcracker." Frieda embraced the nutcracker, placed it gently on the table next to her bed, took one final glance, and hurried back to work.

❧ Law and Order ❧

The Court House

Constable Ferdinand Clutt (Fred Clutt, the ice man's first cousin), kept law and order in the town of Pleasantville. If someone stole a few chickens, or helped himself to a cord of firewood ... if a fellow townsman became a bit unruly under the influence, the event was reported to Constable Clutt. Assuming the individual at fault was identified, then the Constable would come around and escort that person to the home of the Justice of the Peace, Don Pentin. It might be noted that his father, Horace, was the town lawyer and although Don never attended law school, he knew a lot of the law from his dad.

The Justice of the Peace would set bail in minor cases, but in the case of a felony, Constable Clutt would usher the guilty party to jail, which consisted of four cells and was located in the cellar of the Court House. In a situation when one of the townsfolk had a little too much to drink, they'd let him sleep it off overnight in one of the empty cells.

The Court House, which was built in 1887, was the hub of public services. The County Judge had his office on the first floor, to the right as you walked in. The courtroom was straight down the hall. Todd Hinkley, the County Treasurer, had his office way in the back on the second floor. Mr. Hinkley was a meek and quiet man, so quiet and so meek that no one ever knew when he was there or he wasn't there. He kept getting re-elected because folks assumed that anyone so quiet and sober must be trustworthy and able.

❧ A Couple of Items of Interest ❧
11

Two items of particular note to our readers appeared in the December 22, 1893 *Gazette*. They appeared on two different pages but are inexorably related.

Page 1. Column 3.
Miss May McCadden, teacher of the third and fourth grades, has resigned, her resignation taking effect on Friday, December 29, 1893.

Page 4. Column 2.
Mr. Robert Helt, Pleasantville village smithy, and Miss May McCadden, highly regarded teacher, were married in Pleasantville Monday morning, the Reverend Edwin Littlefield officiating.

❧ A Postscript ❧

As Clarke Sanford wrote in the Christmas edition of the *Gazette*:

Before the next issue of the Gazette reaches you, our readers, and the next bits of news and happenings of our town are told, Christmas will have come and gone.

Anticipating the spirit of good fellowship that reaches its peak on Christmas Day, we beg to join in the many expressions of good will and good cheer and extend to every reader our sincere and hearty wish for A Merry Christmas.

We'll see you in Pleasantville next Christmas. Just remember, any time you are in town, stop in and let us know how you are and give us the latest news.

YOU ARE
LEAVING

PLEASANTVILLE

COME BACK
SOON

Some of the Pleasantville Population

Orson B. Allaben .... published first Pleasantville newspaper, The Utilitarian
Clyde and Clara Ashbey .... current owners Pleasantville Hotel
    1 daughter - Uly
Mr. and Mrs. George Ashbey .... Pleasantville Hotel founders
Miss Louise Baker .... Rose Gerber's sister
Sadie Baker .... Rose Gerber's and Louise Baker's mother;
    donated harmonium to the Methodist Church
Samuel Baker .... married to Hannah B. Reade;
    brother-in-law to Sadie and the late Harold Baker
George and Sara Balcomb .... farm family
    4 sons: Matthew, Mark, Luke, and John
Kevin Ballard .... farm hand and fiddle player
W. E. Beals and Mrs. Beals .... second publisher of The Utilitarian
Roselynn Blancgard .... new mother of twins
Ken Brown .... choir master, Methodist Church
Ferdinand Clutt .... Pleasantville Constable
Fred Clutt .... ice man
Leslie Demont .... school janitor, street lamplighter
Fannie Dugan .... dressmaker; shop over The Country Store
Leonard and Sis Finch .... Bob Ruff's sister and brother-in-law
Leonard Finch, Jr. .... employed by Miss Helen Fountain
Fire House horses .... Ole Sam and Barney
Miss Helen Fountain .... owns the boarding house in Pleasantville
Rose and Sam Gerber .... live in the blue-grey house on Orchard St.
    2 sons: Toddy and Carl
    cat: Harry
    dog: Skip
Earl and Betty Gorsch .... owners of the Country Store
Elizabeth Grey .... new mother
Elizabeth Haltendorf .... sister of Dr. Louis Haltendorf
Dr. Louis Haltendorf .... new physician in Pleasantville
Celly Hartshone .... Flower Committee Chairman

Mrs. Heley	Presbyterian Church goer
Bob Helt	village blacksmith
Mr. and Mrs. Billy Hendricks and 2 children	moved to New York City
George Hendricks	current Fire Chief
Todd Hinkley	County Treasurer
John Hitt	County Supervisor
Charlie and Jeanette Hubbard	owners of Pleasantville Bakery
A. Adam Hudgins	former registrar at the State Prison
Horace Jenkins	oldest voter in the County
Lester Le Puis	picked up school children in his wagon
Reverend Edwin and Emily Littlefield	Minister of Presbyterian Church
2 sons: Glen and Oswald	
Josephine Littlefield	librarian
Gerhard and Mary Lou MacMurray	donated original Pleasantville Christmas tree
Miss May McCadden	3rd and 4th grades teacher
George and Carolyn Miller	dairy farmers
2 children: Kitty and Randolph	
Mrs. Murphy	landlady of Miss May McCadden
E. L. O'Connor	Apothecary
Carl Olmsted	mail carrier
Dr. William Olmstead	town Veterinarian
Walt Pattberg	Railroad Station master
Don Pentin	Justice of the Peace, son of Horace
Horace Pentin	town lawyer
Cecil Polley	first chief, Volunteer Fire Department
Cornelia Polley	Cecil's wife; Fire Department's Ladies Auxiliary Committee
Homer Pruzer	partner in Feed Store
Hannah Reed	married to Samuel Baker
Dehlia Robertson	parishioner
Bob and Myrtle Ruff	farm owners
2 sons: Robert, Jr. and Archibald	
Billy Russell	grandson of Frank Russell; current principal of Pleasantville School
Carrie Russell	first librarian
Frank Russell	school teacher

Clarke A. Sanford .... publisher of *Pleasantville Gazette*

Dot and Elmer Sanford (Mr. S) .... toy store owners
  3 children: Thomas, Will and Mary

Norman Sanford .... Railroad crossing guard

Pearl Simpson .... eloped with Dr. Louis Haltendorf

Dr. Squires .... Pleasantville physician

Henry Sutter .... owner, Sutter Bros. Saloon

Bob Taylor .... country singer and songwriter

William Todd (Shorty) .... town barber, on the sick list

Mrs. L. J. Tompkins .... under the weather

Burt Tubbs .... founder of the Department Store, raises bees

John Tubbs .... Burt's son and current Department Store owner

John Jr. and Clarissa Tubbs .... John's son and daughter-in-law,
                                                                    he works in the Department Store
  2 children: Glen and Margaret

Miss Frieda Van Fuern .... church goer; works for Dr. Squires

Minister and Mrs. Russell Warden .... Minister of the Methodist Church
  1 daughter: Rebecca Jane

Miss Zena Warden .... sister of the Minister; 1st and 2nd grades teacher

Floyd and Minnie Welch .... partner in Feed Store
                                                            Minnie is the mother of six daughters

Sexton Wooten .... official of the Presbyterian Church, ringer of the bells

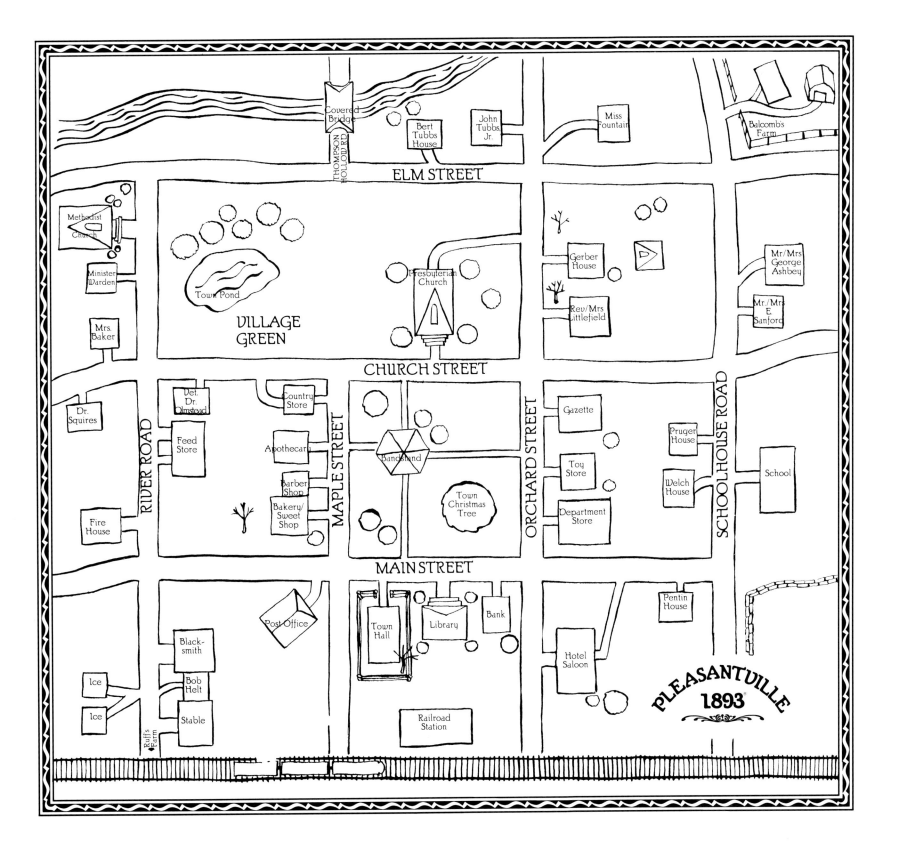

A special thank you to Dick S. and The Catskill Mountain News as a valuable source. Thank you, also, to Bob Helt and George Balcomb for inspiration and thank you to everyone who has contributed in any way to this brief history of **Pleasantville, 1893**.